POPSTARS

Exclusive distributors:
Music Sales Limited, 8/9 Frith Street, London W1D 3JB, England.
Music Sales Pty Limited, 120 Rothschild Avenue, Rosebery, NSW 2018, Australia.

Order No. AM971201. ISBN 0-7119-8953-2. This book © Copyright 2001 by Wise Publications.

Your Guarantee of Quality:
As publishers, we strive to produce every book to the highest commercial standards.
The music has been freshly engraved and, whilst endeavouring to retain the original running order of the recorded album,
the book has been carefully designed to minimise awkward page turns and to make playing from it a real pleasure.
Particular care has been given to specifying acid-free, neutral-sized paper made from pulps which have not been elemental chlorine bleached.
This pulp is from farmed sustainable forests and was produced with special regard for the environment.
Throughout, the printing and binding have been planned to ensure a sturdy, attractive publication which should give years of enjoyment.
If your copy fails to meet our high standards, please inform us and we will gladly replace it.

Music Sales' complete catalogue describes thousands of titles and is available in full colour sections by subject, direct from
Music Sales Limited. Please state your areas of interest and send a cheque/postal order for £1.50 for postage to:
Music Sales Limited, Newmarket Road, Bury St. Edmunds, Suffolk IP33 3YB.

www.musicsales.com

Wise Publications
London/New York/Sydney/Paris/Copenhagen/Madrid/Tokyo

PURE AND SIMPLE

Words & Music by Tim Hawes, Pete Kirtley & Alison Clarkson

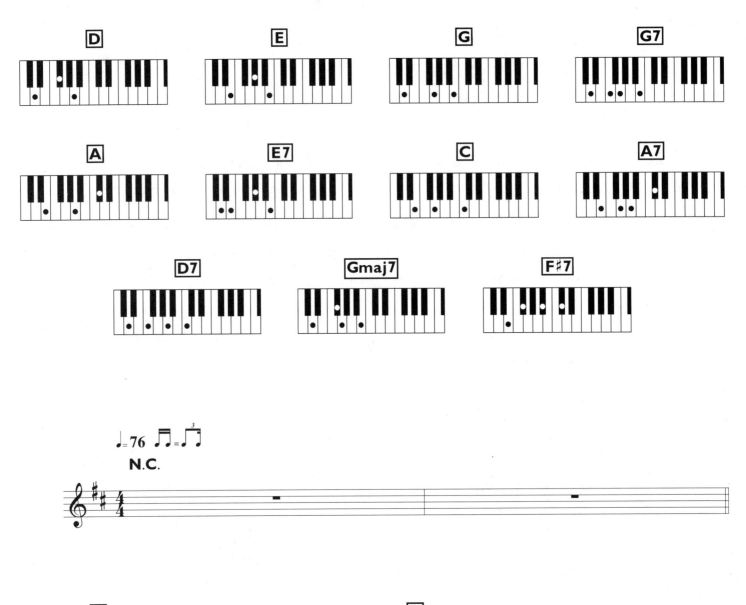

1. You been say-ing I'm driv-ing you cra-zy and I have-n't been a-round for you late-ly,
(Verse 2 see block lyric)

but I had a few things on my mind.____

When I'm with you I am filled with e-mo-tion, can't you see that I'm giv-ing you de-vo-tion

and a love like this is hard to find.

I know I've been a-walk-ing a-round in a daze. (Ba-by, ba-by.)

You got-ta be-lieve me when I say (Ah ooh ooh) Where-ev-er you

go. (I'm gon-na be there) what-ev-er you do, (You know I'm gon-na be there. it's pure and

sim-ple, (Oh yeah yeah.) I'll be there for you. (Pure and sim-ple gon-na be there.) What-ev-er it

takes, (I'm gon-na be there.) I swear it's true, (You know I'm gon-na be there. it's pure and

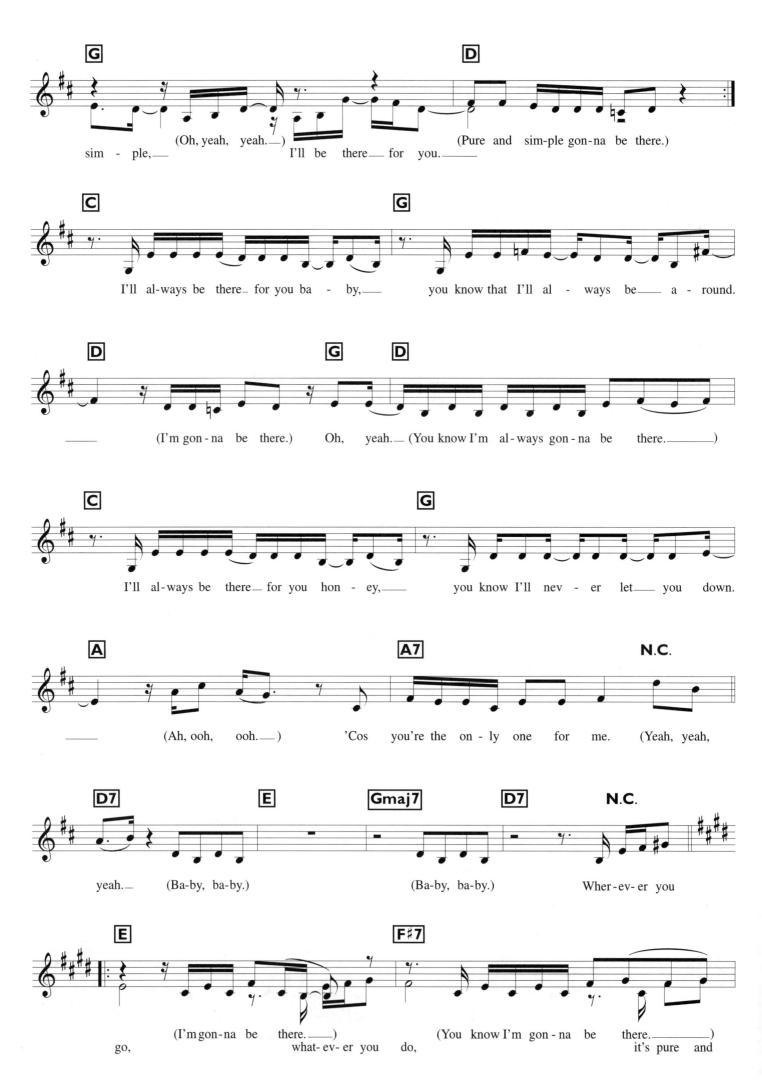

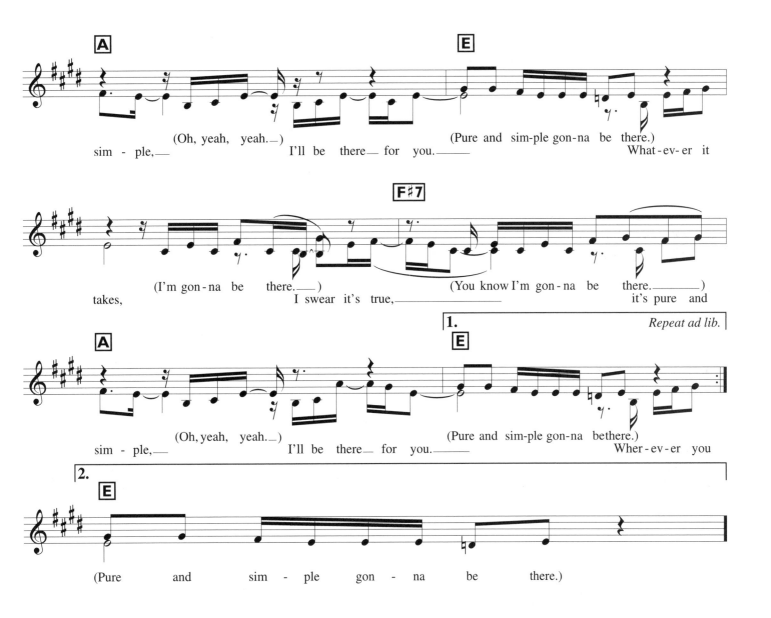

Verse 2:
I'll be there through the stormiest weather
Always trying to make things a bit better
And I know I gotta try and get through to you
You can love me in a way like no other
But the situation's taking you under
So you need to tell me now what you wanna do.

I know I've been walking around in a daze (Baby, baby)
You gotta believe me when I say (Ah, ooh, ooh)

Wherever you go *etc.*

THE WAY TO YOUR LOVE

Words & Music by Mikkel SE, Hallgeir Rustan & Tor Erik Hermansen

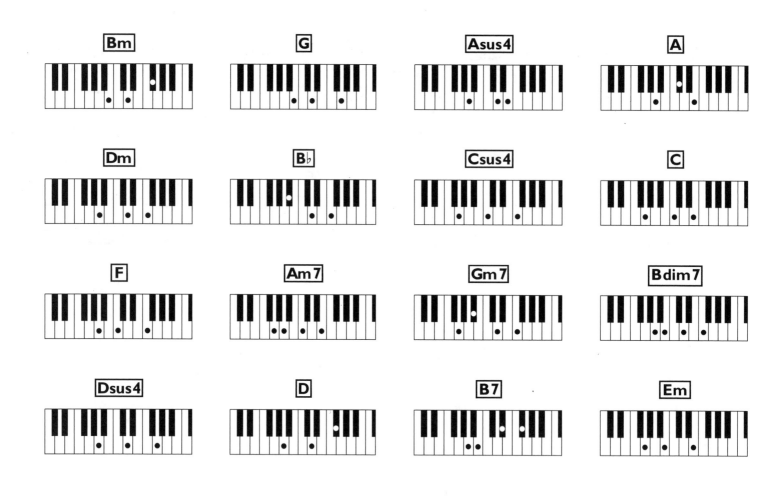

1. I can

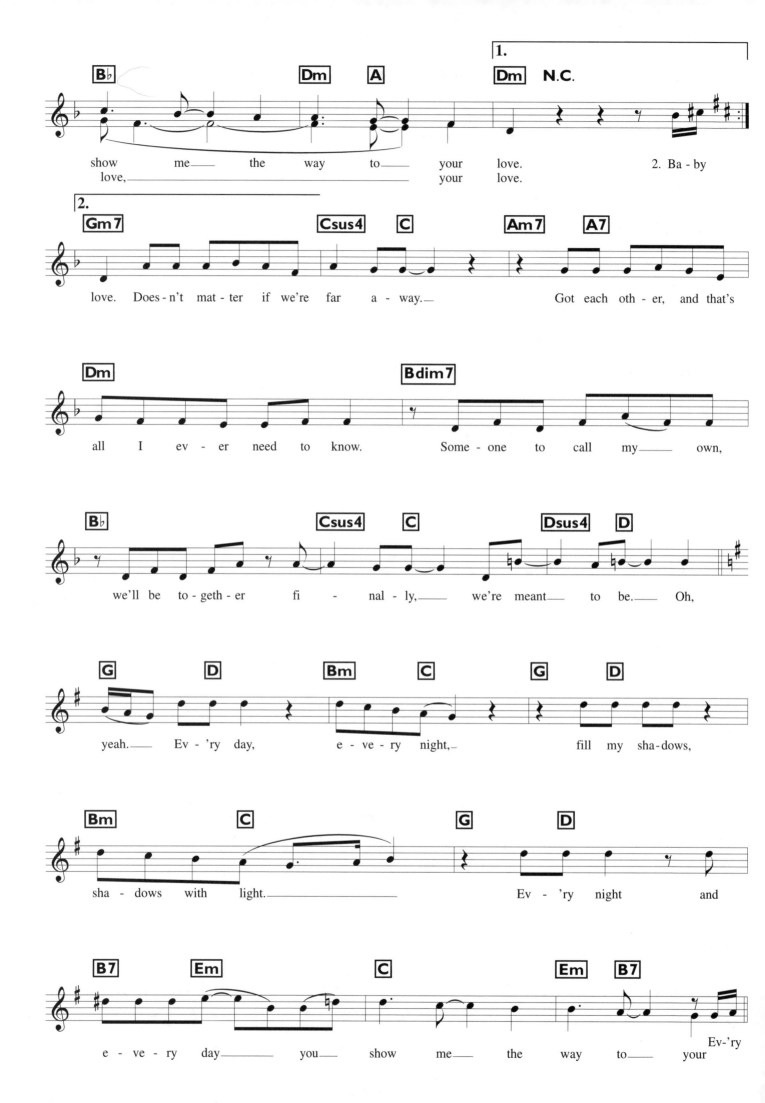

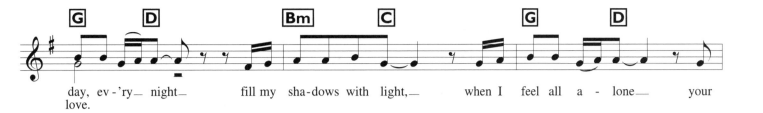

day, ev-'ry— night— fill my sha-dows with light,— when I feel all a - lone— your
love.

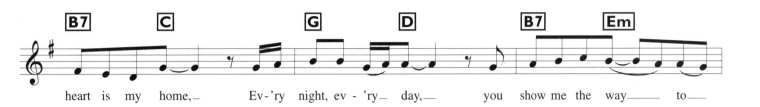

heart is my home,— Ev-'ry night, ev - 'ry— day,— you show me the way—— to—

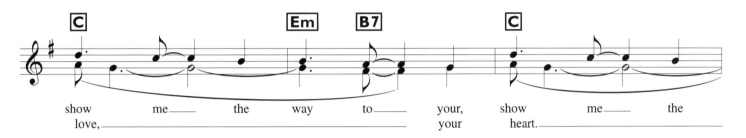

show me— the way to—— your, show me— the
love, your heart.

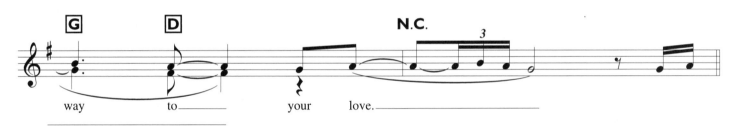

way to— your love.

Verse 2:
Baby now that I've found you
Realise I was lost
Didn't know love could treat me this way
Maybe what it comes down to
When it matters the most
Is to find joy in every day.

We could sink to the bottom
We could climb to the top
'Cos together we'll never give up.

Every day, every night *etc.*

ANOTHER LOVER

Words & Music by Henry Binns & Yoyo Olugbo

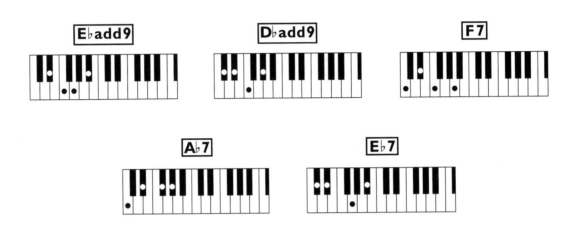

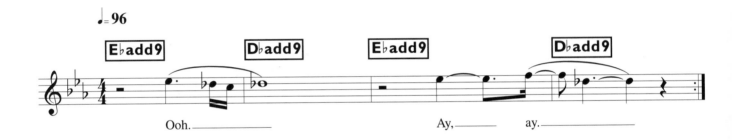

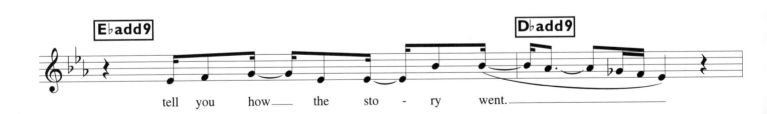

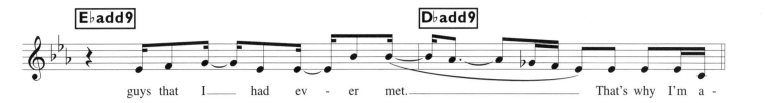

E♭add9   D♭add9

guys that I___ had ev - er met._____ That's why I'm a -

E♭add9   D♭add9

- hold - ing tight ev - 'ry night   I go out - ta my mind

(Verse 2 see block lyric)

E♭add9   D♭add9

think - ing 'bout where you could be,   no you're not___ with me.

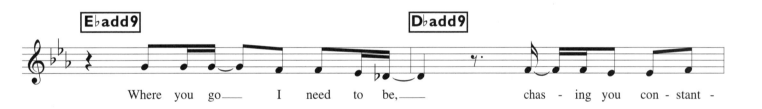

E♭add9   D♭add9

Where you go___ I need to be,___   chas - ing you con - stant -

E♭add9   D♭add9

- ly.___ In - stead I be - lieve___   that's___ why___

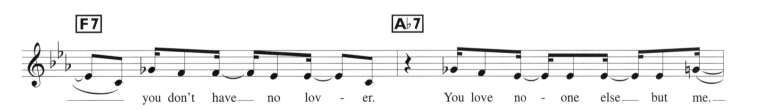

F7   A♭7

___ you don't have___ no lov - er.   You love no - one else___ but me.___

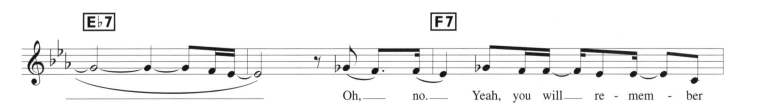

E♭7   F7

_____ Oh,___ no.___ Yeah, you will re - mem - ber

you see no - one else — but me. — Eeh.

1.

Ooh. — Ay, — ay. — 2. All I ev -

2.

He don't have no lov - er, he loves no - one else but — me. —

Eeh. Girl you must re-mem - ber he sees no - one else but —

— me. — That's why I'm-a hold - ing tight ev - 'ry night.

I go out - ta my mind think - ing 'bout where you could be.

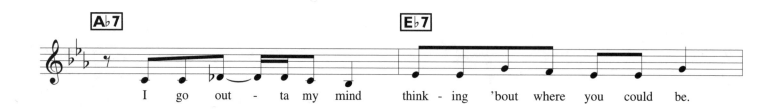

Oh, yeah. — Oh, yeah. — Where you go — I need to be, —

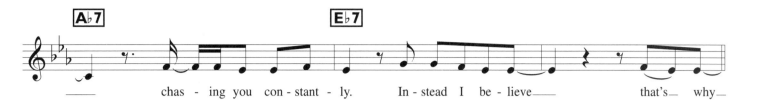

chas - ing you con - stant - ly. In - stead I be - lieve___ that's___ why___

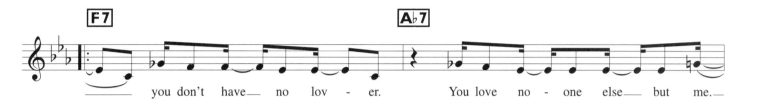

___ you don't have___ no lov - er. You love no - one else___ but me.___

Yeah, you will___ re - mem - ber

Repeat ad lib.

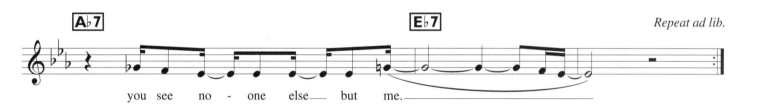

you see no - one else___ but me.___

Repeat to fade

Ooh.___ Ay,___ ay.___

Verse 2:
All I ever wanted was someone to show me
What it could be like and would feel like to be
As soon as I discovered there is nothing better
My baby and me.

And that's why *etc.*

ONE

Words & Music by Mikkel SE, Hallgeir Rustan & Tor Erik Hermansen

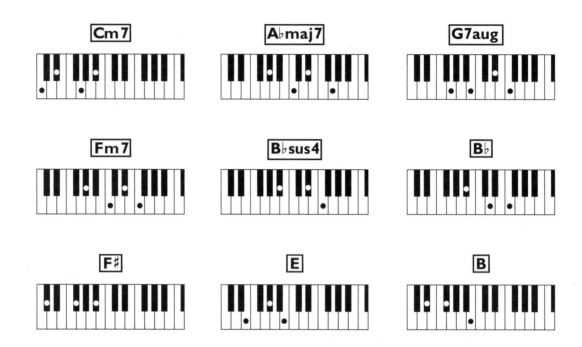

1. Ev-'ry-time I get a lit-tle pres-sure from you,—— stress-in' 'bout the things that you wan-na do,——
(Verse 2 see block lyric)

talk-ing like we could have been, should have been here, (here) there, (there) ev - 'ry - where.

You got-ta re-al-ise I'm not the kind of girl___ who wan-na be a-lone in this cra-zy world,

___ that I'm not a-look-ing for the kind of man___ who does-n't un-der-stand.___

'Cos all I need___ is some-bo-dy, some-one who can come and dance___ at my par-ty.

All I real-ly want is some - one who's got it, 'cos I'm not look-ing for the one.

'Cos all I need___ is some-bo-dy, some-one who'll-be get-ting down___ at my par-ty.

All I real - ly want is some - one who's got it, 'cos I'm not look-ing for the one.

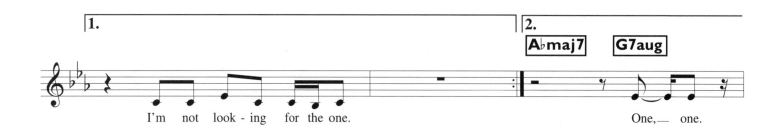

I'm not look-ing for the one.
One,— one.

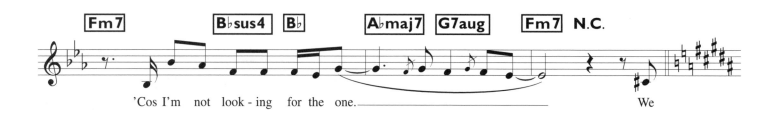

'Cos I'm not look-ing for the one._____ We

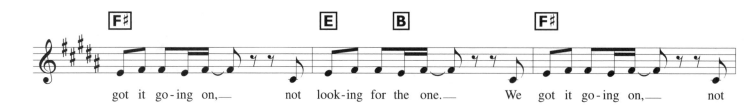

got it go-ing on,— not look-ing for the one.— We got it go-ing on,— not

look-ing for the one.— We got it go-ing on,— not look-ing for the one.— We

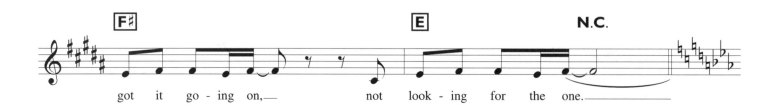

got it go - ing on,— not look - ing for the one._____

___ 'Cos all I need— is some-bo-dy, some-one who can come and dance— at my par-ty.

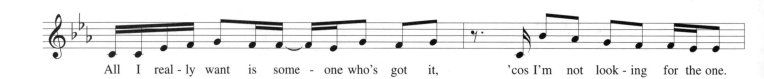

All I real-ly want is some - one who's got it, 'cos I'm not look-ing for the one.

16

'Cos all I need— is some-bo-dy, some-one who'll be get-ting down— at my par-ty.

All I real-ly want is some - one who's got it, 'cos I'm not look-ing for the one.

'Cos all I need— is some-bo-dy, some-one who can come and dance— at my par-ty.

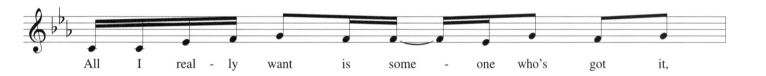

All I real - ly want is some - one who's got it,

'cos I'm not look - ing for the one.

Verse 2:
If you think I'm gonna get serious
I'm talking 'bout the ring for the two of us
Better give it up, don't be ridiculous
'Cos you've missed the bus
You gotta realise I'm not the kind of guy
Giving you my promises to qualify
Baby even though you got it going on
Don't mean that you're the one.

'Cos all I need *etc*.

NOT THE KIND

Words & Music by Mikkel SE, Hallgeir Rustan, Tor Erik Hermansen & Cathy Dennis

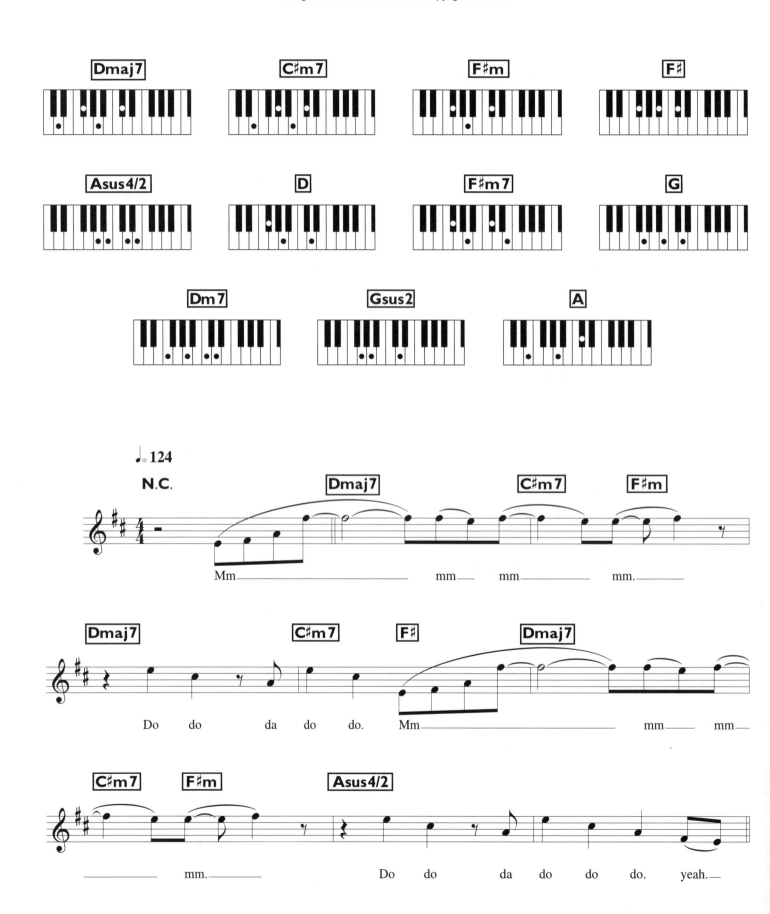

the kind of girl who would play a - round. Well I'm not the kind of guy who would

let you down. So you're not that kind of guy, so you're not that kind of girl. We're

good when we're to - ge - ther but it's hard when we're a - part. Mm mm mm

mm. Do do da do do. Mm mm mm

Repeat ad lib.

1.

mm. Do do da do do do. Well I'm not

2.

We're good when we're to - ge - ther but it's hard when we're a - part, yeah!

Verse 2:
I'm not the jealous kind
But you've been playing with my mind
In every single way
I think about you every day
When I'm alone I just worry about you
You say you love me boy, so why should I doubt you.

Everybody wants to have a boy like you *etc.*

MAKE IT HAPPEN

Words & Music by Ray Hedges, Nigel Butler, Myleene Klass, Noel Sullivan & Suzanne Shaw

know that I am gon-na wait I'm gon-na take my time.— (I'm gon-na take my time.————) There's

no need to an-ti-ci-pate, I'm gon-na make you mine.— (Make— you mine.————)

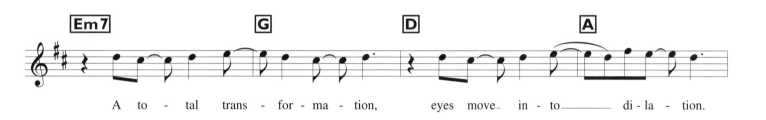

A to-tal trans-for-ma-tion, eyes move— in-to———— di-la-tion.

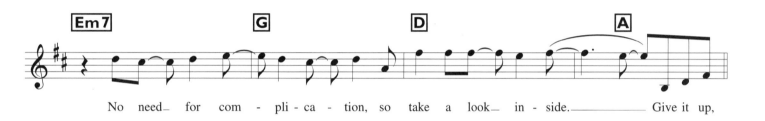

No need— for com-pli-ca-tion, so take a look— in-side.———————— Give it up,

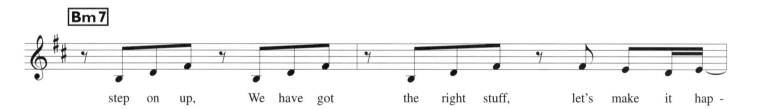

step on up, We have got the right stuff, let's make it hap-

- pen. Give it up,
(Shake your rhy-thm now feel the mo-tion, shake your rhy-thm you've got the mo-tion.)

step on out. I know where,— you know how,— let's make it hap-

Verse 2:
Movin' through the crowd I can feel you
Need you by my side
Feel your body move through night into morning
Just enjoy the ride.

You know that I am gonna wait *etc.*

ONE STEP CLOSER

Words & Music by Ray Hedges, Nigel Butler, Danny Foster & Kym Marsh

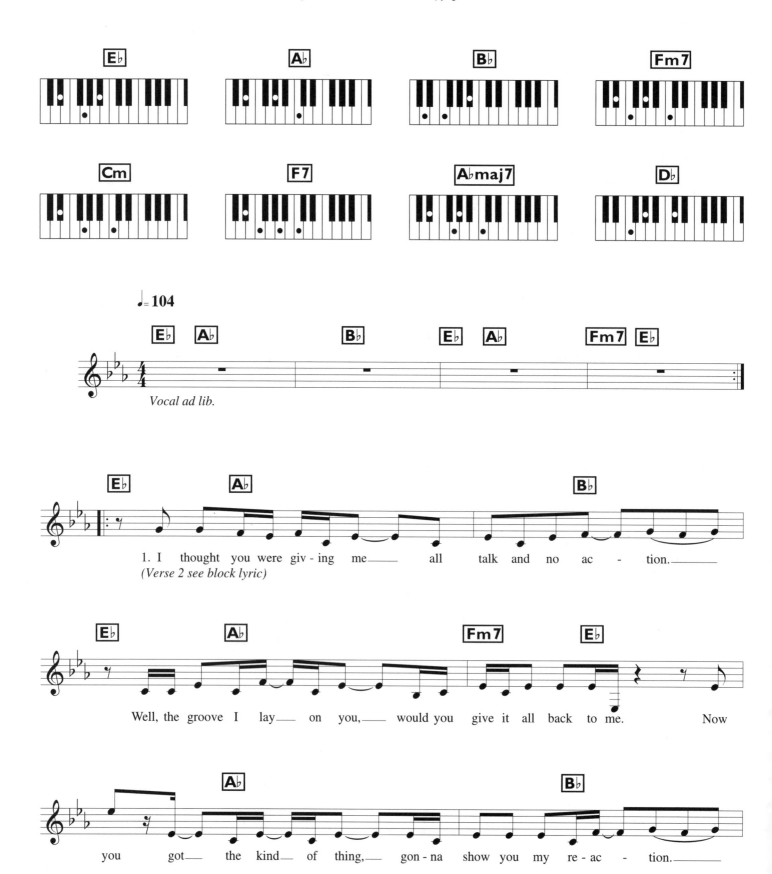

1. I thought you were giv-ing me___ all talk and no ac - tion.___
(Verse 2 see block lyric)

Well, the groove I lay___ on you,___ would you give it all back to me. Now

you got___ the kind___ of thing,___ gon - na show you my re - ac - tion.___

Doo dap da doo da. Doo dap da doo da. It's gon - na take some time.

(Hey, hey, hey, hey.) I've got you on my mind. It's what I

need. It's gon - na take some time. It's what I need. I've got you on my mind.

What you've got____ is what I need.____ It's got my mind_

____ run - ning ov - er - time.____ What you've got____ is what I need.

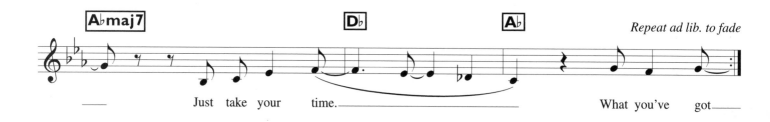

Repeat ad lib. to fade

____ Just take your time.____ What you've got____

Verse 2:
Hey, boy if you're wantin' me better get yourself together
If you step too close to me gonna do what I gotta do
Now you make me feel so right with a sweeter satisfaction
Give it up and get it on 'cos the hustle is overdue.

It's just one drop in the ocean *etc.*

MYLEENE KLASS

DANNY FOSTER

KYM MARSH

SUZANNE SHAW

NOEL SULLIVAN

hear'say

CARRIED AWAY

Words & Music by Ray Hedges, Tracy Ackerman & Martin Brannigan

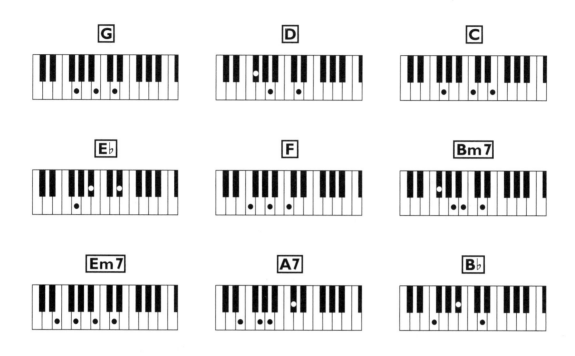

1. Once a-gain I lie a-wake at night in sto-ry-land, I'm
(Verse 2 see block lyric)

slip-ping a-way. Un-der-stand, just to es-cape I run to hope,

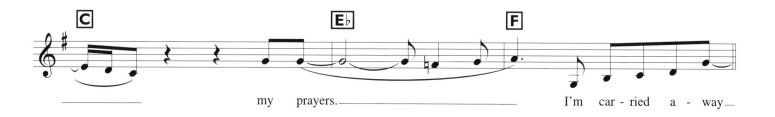

my prayers. I'm car-ried a - way

your e - ter - nal flame, don't blow it out.

You got - ta leave it on. I'm car - ried a - way,

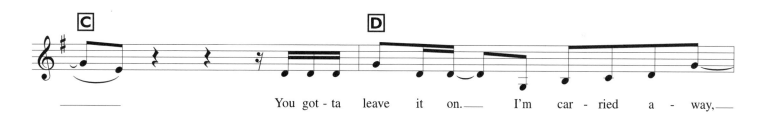

I'm find - ing my faith goes on and on,

Repeat to fade

I'm real - ly get - ting car - ried a - way. I'm car - ried a - way

Verse 2:
Never fall into the world of someone calling out
A mirror inside
Is telling me you're just a breath away from doubt
And you wake in the night.

I'm sinking in the sand *etc.*

BREATHE

Words & Music by Mikkel SE, Hallgeir Rustan & Tor Erik Hermansen

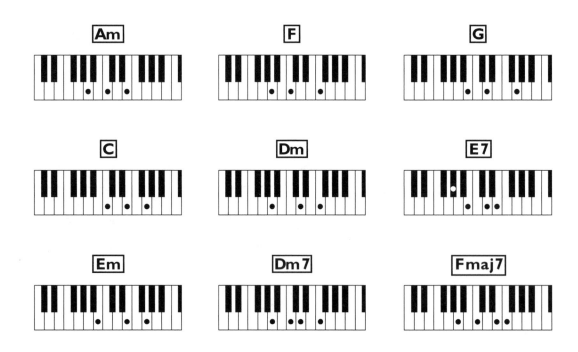

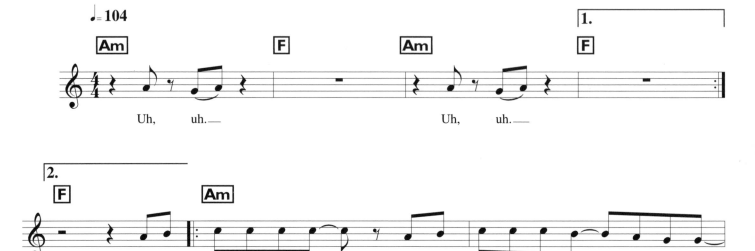

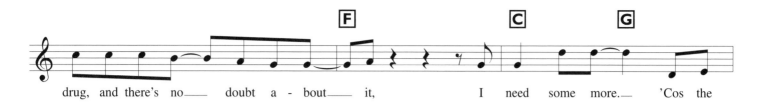

drug, and there's no ____ doubt a - bout ____ it, I need some more. 'Cos the

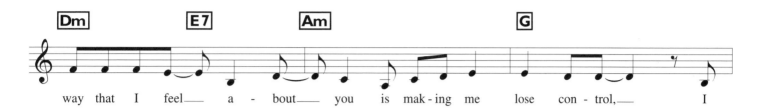

way that I feel ____ a - bout ____ you is mak - ing me lose con - trol, ____ I

want it all. A - ny - where ____ you go, ba - by, I'll ____ fol - low. I will find ____

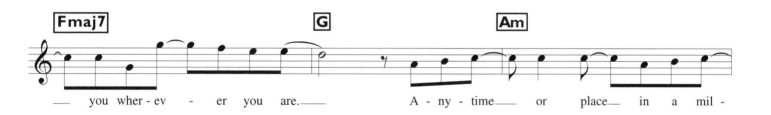

____ you wher - ev - er you are. ____ A - ny - time ____ or place ____ in a mil -

- lion ways. ____ I need ____ you like e - ve - ry breath ____ I take.

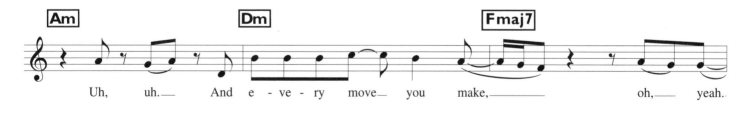

Uh, uh. ____ And e - ve - ry move ____ you make, ____ oh, ____ yeah.

1. **2.**

____ 2. Ev - en ____ Uh, uh. ____

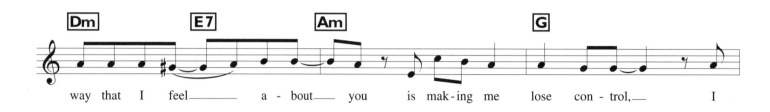

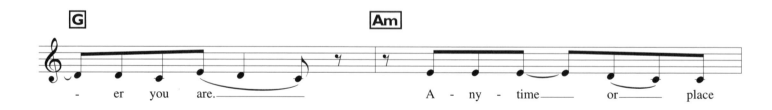

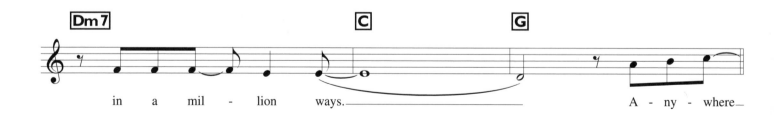

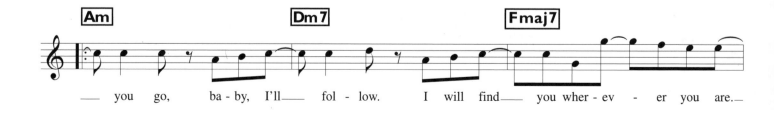

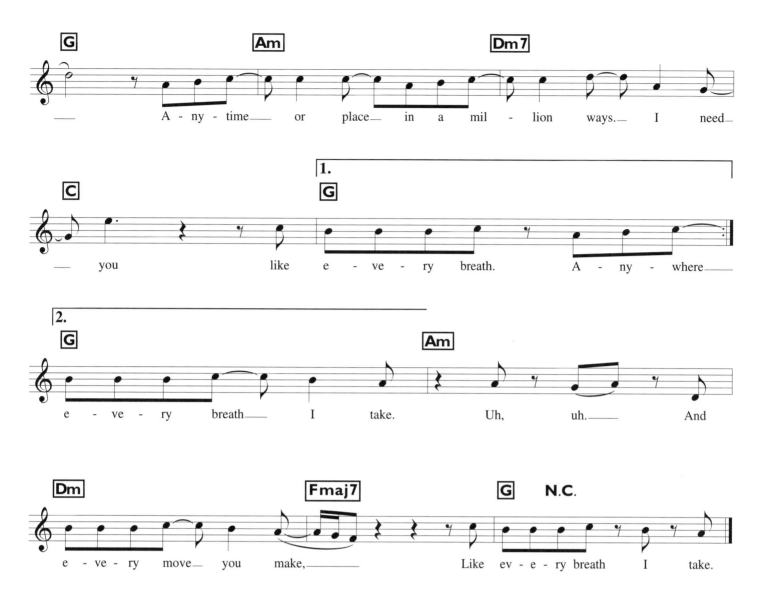

Verse 2:
Even if I would try
There's no way I could ever deny it
I want you near
More than words can explain
There's no letters invented to write it
Anywhere.

'Cos the way that I feel *etc.*

SWEET ALIBI

Words & Music by Ray Hedges, Nigel Butler & Tracy Ackerman

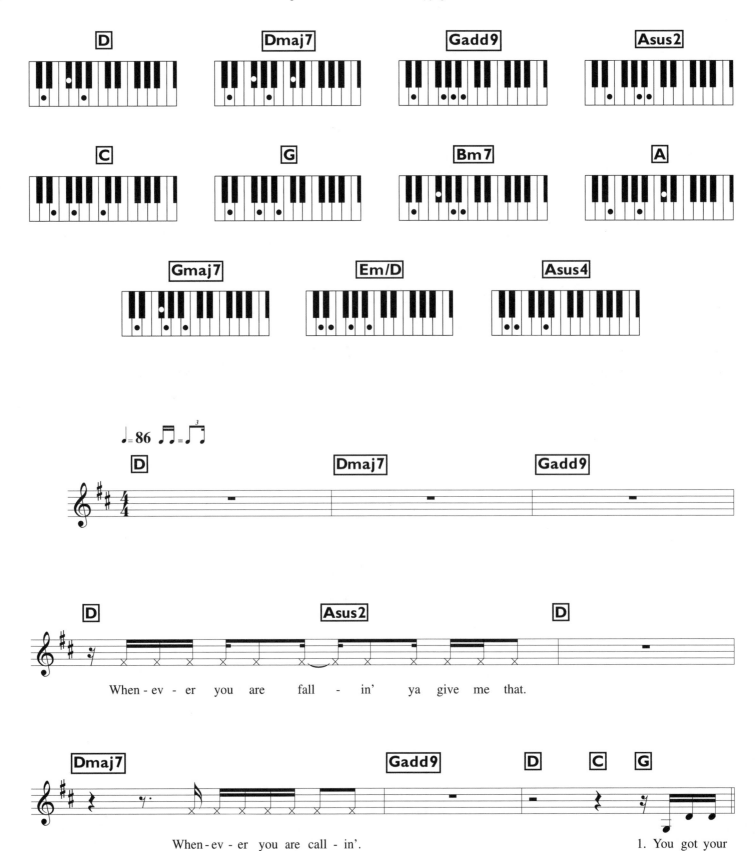

When - ev - er you are fall - in' ya give me that.

When - ev - er you are call - in'.

1. You got your

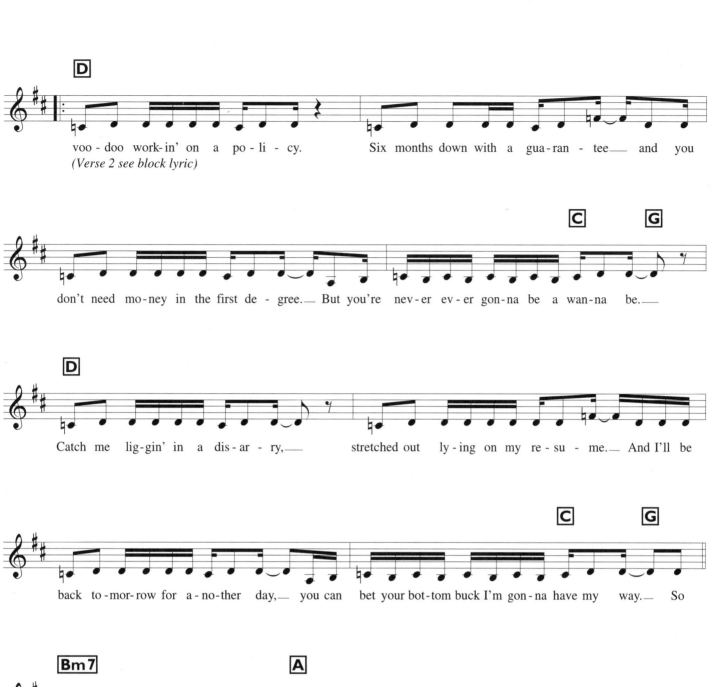

voo-doo work-in' on a po-li-cy. Six months down with a gua-ran-tee___ and you
(Verse 2 see block lyric)

don't need mo-ney in the first de-gree.__ But you're nev-er ev-er gon-na be a wan-na be.__

Catch me lig-gin' in a dis-ar-ry,___ stretched out ly-ing on my re-su-me.__ And I'll be

back to-mor-row for a-no-ther day,__ you can bet your bot-tom buck I'm gon-na have my way.__ So

why,_____ we'll al-ways stay__ to-geth-er ba-by.

Why,_____ be-cause it was al-ways meant__ to be._____ You give me that

sweet a-li-bi.
(Gim-me that, gim-me that.) When-ev-er you are

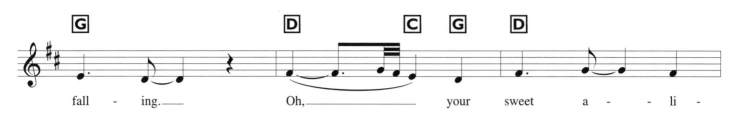

fall - ing.___ Oh,_____ your sweet a - li -

- bi.
(Sweet a - li - bi, got - ta know what you do when you were call - ing___)

You were call - ing___

by._____

2. Got your

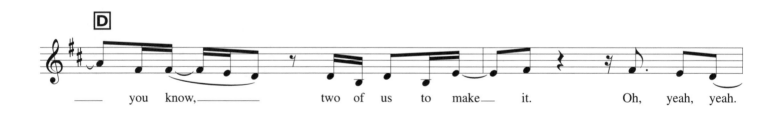

I'm gon - na make a rule___ and break___ it. It takes two,

___ you know,_____ two of us to make___ it. Oh, yeah, yeah.

___ And hea - ven knows I try___ to take___ it. You give me

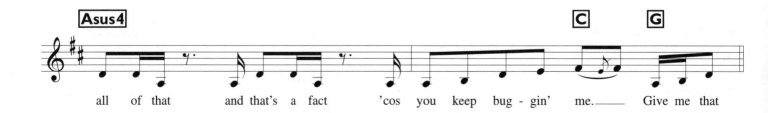

all of that and that's a fact 'cos you keep bug - gin' me.___ Give me that

sweet a - li - bi.
(Sweet a - li - bi got - ta know what you do when you were

fall - - - ing._____ Oh,_____ your

sweet a - li - bi.
(Sweet a - li - bi, got - ta know what you do when you were

Repeat to fade

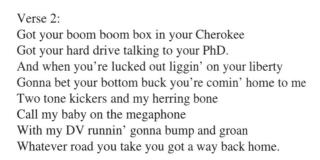

call - - - ing_____ by._____

Verse 2:
Got your boom boom box in your Cherokee
Got your hard drive talking to your PhD.
And when you're lucked out liggin' on your liberty
Gonna bet your bottom buck you're comin' home to me
Two tone kickers and my herring bone
Call my baby on the megaphone
With my DV runnin' gonna bump and groan
Whatever road you take you got a way back home.

So why *etc.*

COLOUR BLIND

Words & Music by Steve Lee, Avril Mackintosh & Wayne Wilkins

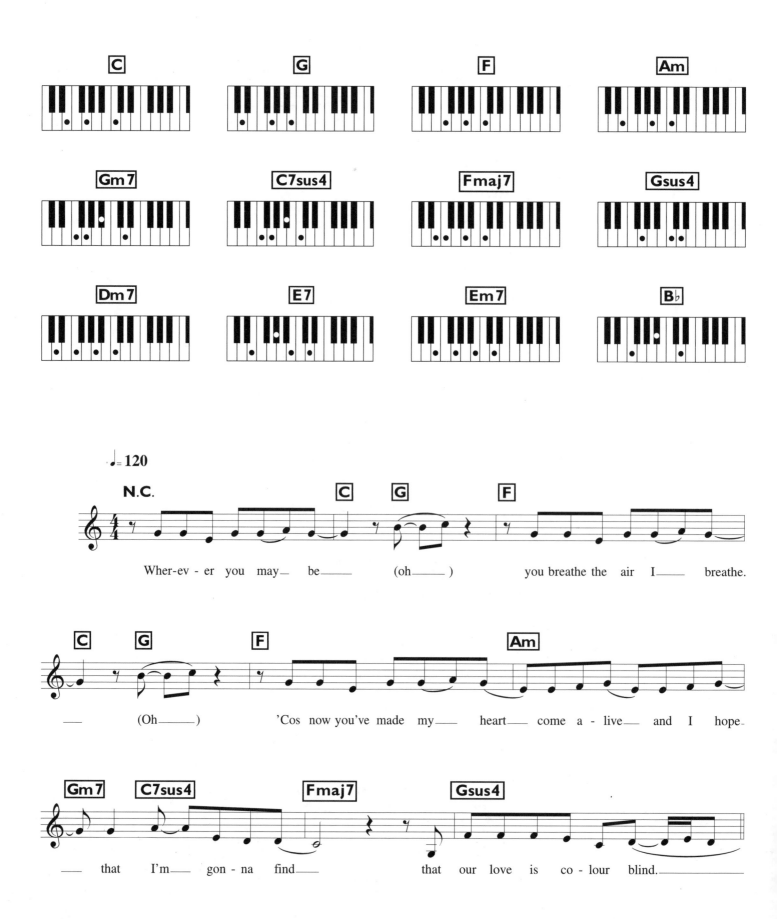

1. They say. "what's the world com-ing to?" Tell me what

chance is there for me and you? It's not e-nough to be-lieve that love is

blind._____

2. You say our
(Verse 3 see block lyric)

fu-ture's-gon-na be so bright. Tell me that ev-'ry-thing will be al-right.

But I need to be-lieve you'll op-en up your mind.

You and I can be_____ to-ge-ther but we both know_____ that

love can't live a lie._____ Wher-ev-er you may_____ be_____

(oh___) you breathe the air I___ breathe.___ (Oh.___)

But if the world you___ see is black and white___ then I might___ just___ blow___ your___ mind.

___ Yeah, life can be so___ cold,___ (ba - by)

look deep in - side your___ soul,___ (get rea - dy) 'Cos now you've made my___ heart___

___ come a - live___ and I hope___ that I'm___ gon - na find___ that

1, 3. *To Coda* ⊕ **2.**

our love is co - lour blind.___ our love is co - lour blind.___ Takes ev - 'ry kind___

___ of peo - ple to make this world___ go round.___

42

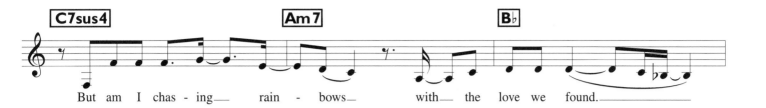

But am I chas - ing___ rain - bows___ with___ the love we found.___

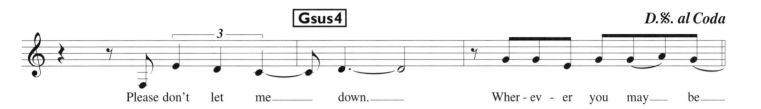

D.%. al Coda

Please don't let me___ down.___ Wher - ev - er you may___ be___

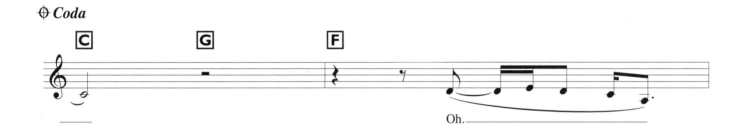

⊕ *Coda*

Oh.___

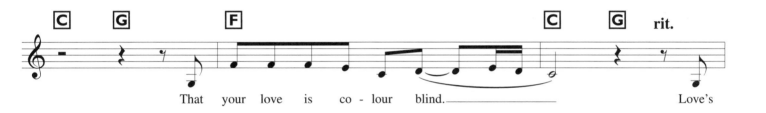

That your love is co - lour blind.___ Love's

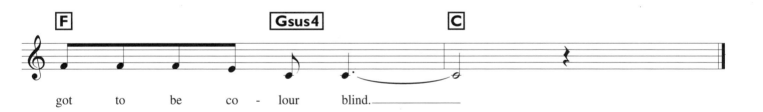

got to be co - lour blind.___

Verse 3:
Now that you and I have come this far
Can we be the people that we think we are?
I need to feel in my heart we'll stand the test of time.

Worlds apart can come together
But look out baby 'cos worlds might still collide.

Wherever you may be *etc.*

LOVE WILL NEVER END

Words & Music by Mikkel SE, Hallgeir Rustan & Tor Erik Hermansen

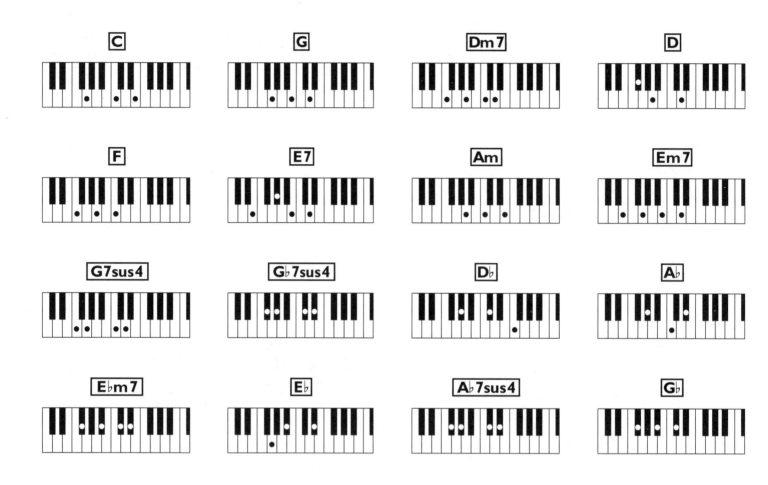

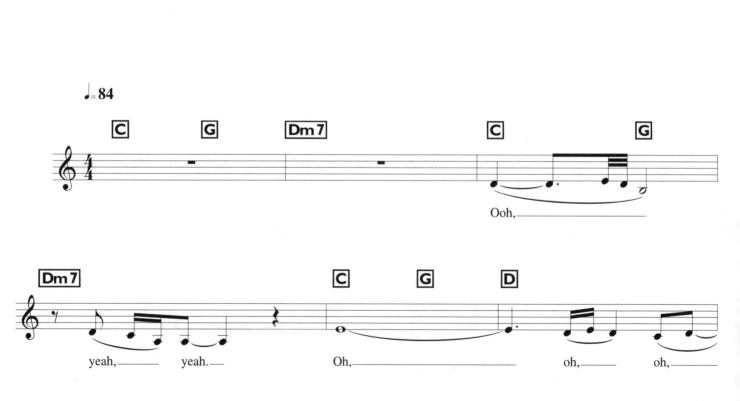

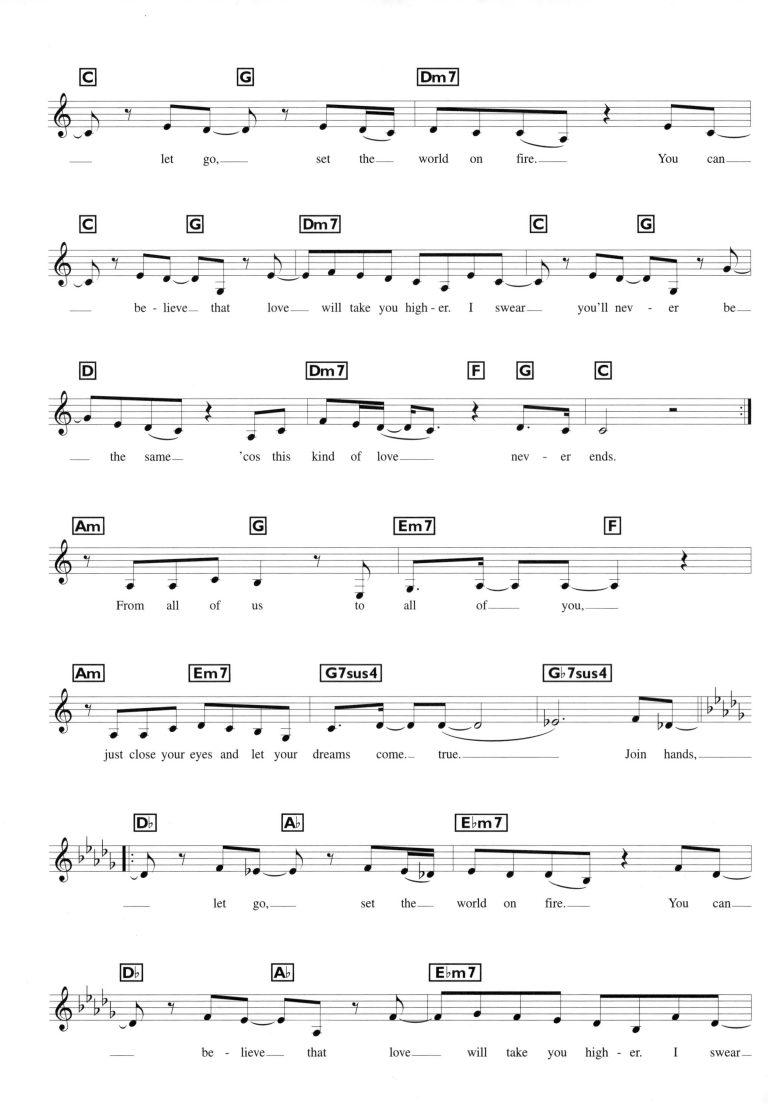

let go, set the world on fire. You can

be - lieve that love will take you high - er. I swear you'll nev - er be

the same 'cos this kind of love nev - er ends.

From all of us to all of you,

just close your eyes and let your dreams come. true. Join hands,

let go, set the world on fire. You can

be - lieve that love will take you high - er. I swear

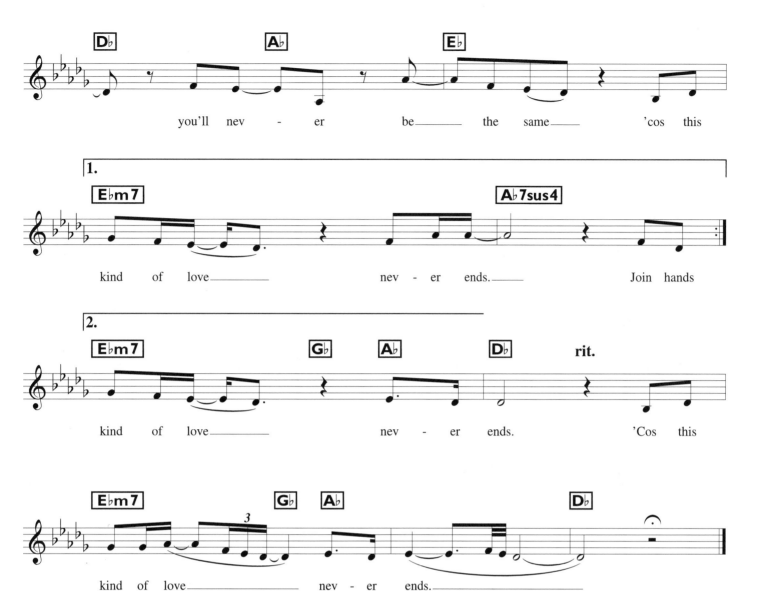

you'll nev - er be the same 'cos this

1.
kind of love nev - er ends. Join hands

2.
kind of love nev - er ends. 'Cos this

kind of love nev - er ends.

Verse 2:
This love is now and forever
I found a way to your heart
Through the sunshine and the rainy days
This much is true
Remember we love you.

Join hands *etc.*

I DIDN'T WANT YOU ANYWAY

Words & Music by Andreas Romdhane, J. Larossi & Rick Mitra

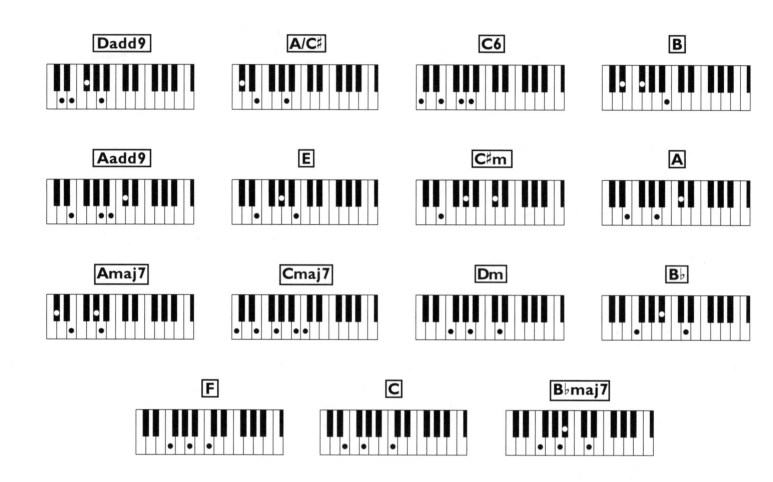

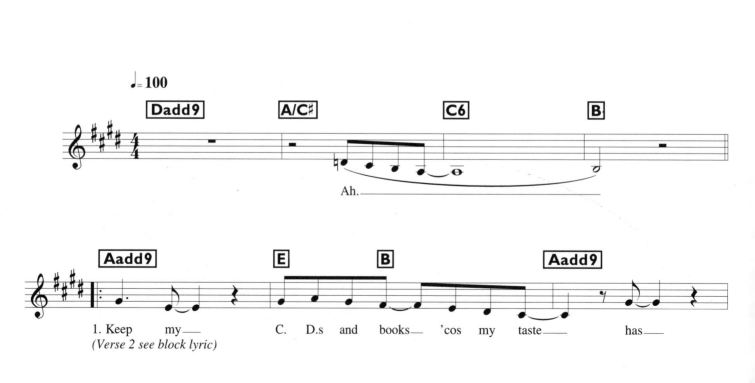

♩ = 100

Ah.

1. Keep my ___ C. D.s and books ___ 'cos my taste ___ has ___

(Verse 2 see block lyric)

changed a - ny - way.— Leave your— wor - ries and trou - bles be - hind—

— with the keys to my place.— You say— that

I'll wor - ry, and I can't let you go — be - fore.—

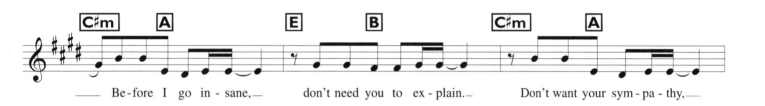

— Be-fore I go in - sane, don't need you to ex - plain.— Don't want your sym - pa - thy,—

got-ta tell you fi - nal - ly.— Be-fore you walk a - way— there's some-thing I need to say,—

— I did - n't want you a - ny - way.—

1.

I did - n't want you a - ny - way.—

Na na na ah ah ah yeah._____

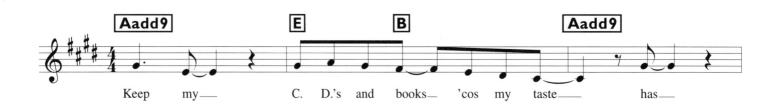

Keep my_____ C. D.'s and books_____ 'cos my taste_____ has_____

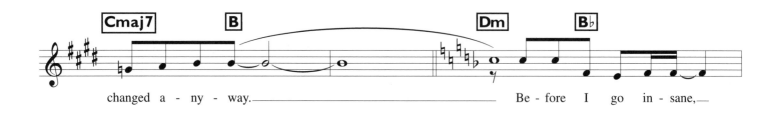

changed a - ny - way._____ Be - fore I go in - sane,_____

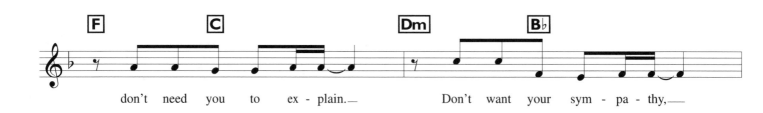

don't need you to ex - plain.___ Don't want your sym - pa - thy,_____

got-ta tell you fin - al - ly.____ Be-fore you walk a - way___ there's some-thing I need to say,___

_____ I did - n't want you a - ny - way.

Verse 2:
Each step was a little bit further away
From what we never had
No you can kid yourself but, oh brother
Can't you see that you're just makin' me mad
You say that you're sorry
It doesn't work anymore, before…
Before I go insane *etc.*

MONDAY MONDAY

Words & Music by John Phillips

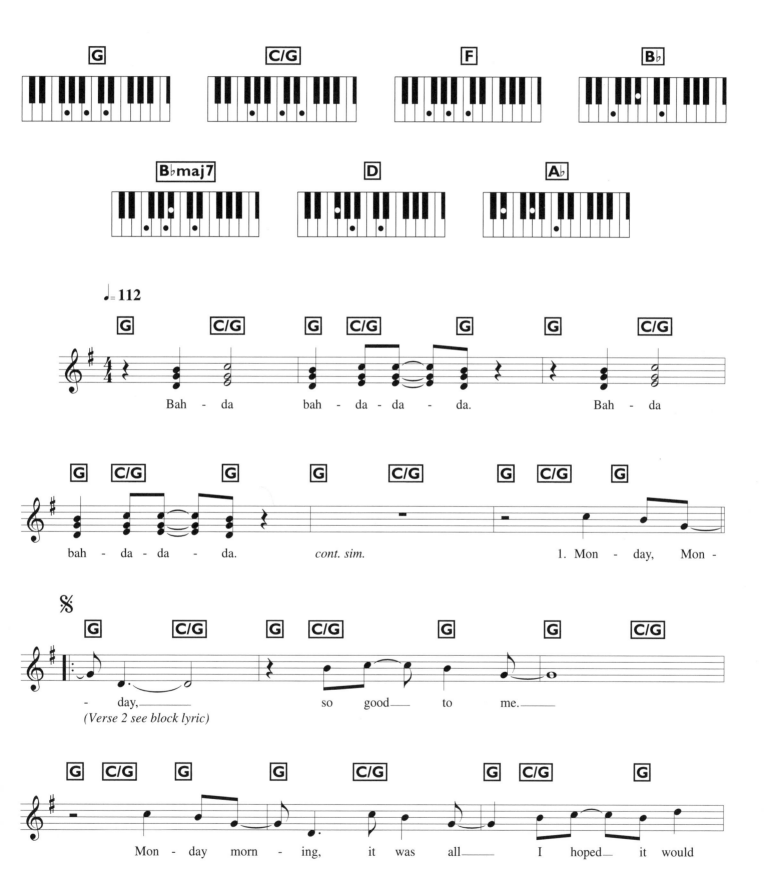

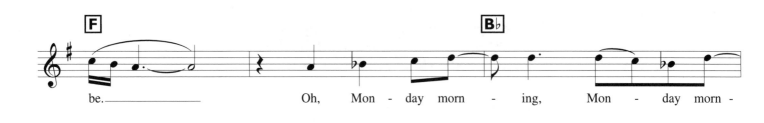

be. Oh, Mon - day morn - ing, Mon - day morn -

ing could - n't guar - an - tee. That Mon - day eve -

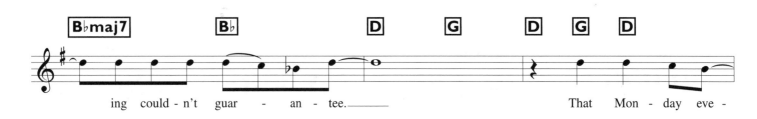

- ning you would still be here with me.

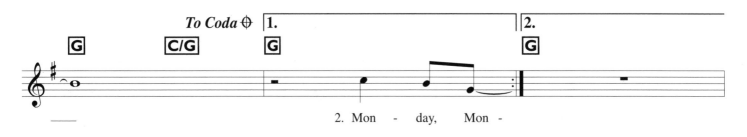

2. Mon - day, Mon -

Ev - 'ry oth - er day, ev - 'ry oth - er day, ev - 'ry oth - er day of the week is

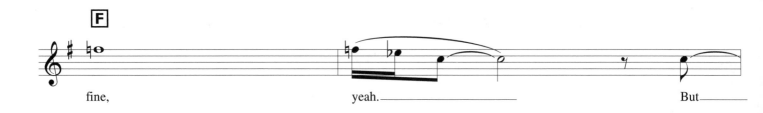

fine, yeah. But

when - ev - er Mon - day comes, but when - ev - er Mon - day comes you can find me

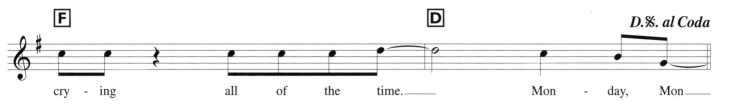

D.%. al Coda

cry - ing all of the time.____ Mon - day, Mon___

⊕ *Coda*

Mon - day, Mon - day.____ Mon - day Mon -

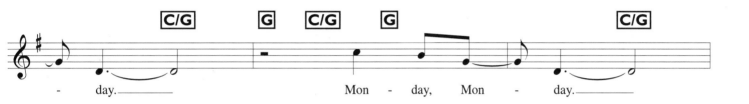

- day.____ Mon - day, Mon - day.____

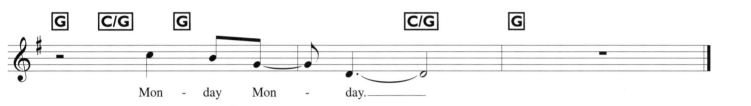

Mon - day Mon - day.____

Verse 2:
Monday, Monday, can't trust that day
Monday, Monday, sometimes it just turns out that way.
Oh, Monday morning gave me no warning of what was to be
Oh, Monday Monday how could you leave and not take me?

BRIDGE OVER TROUBLED WATER

Words & Music by Paul Simon

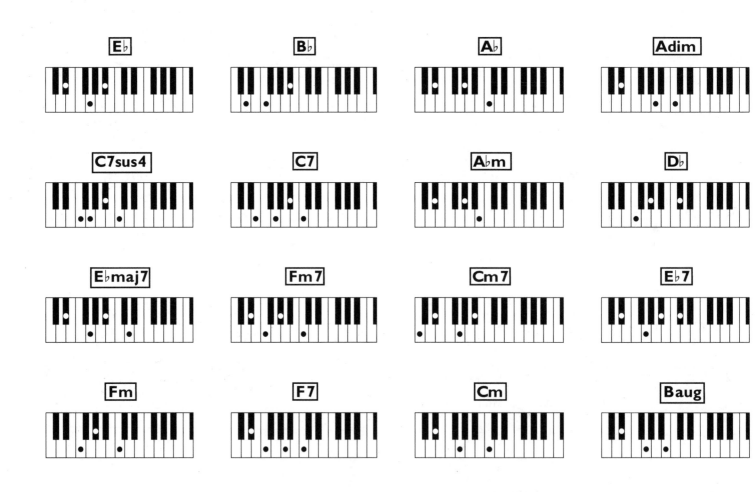

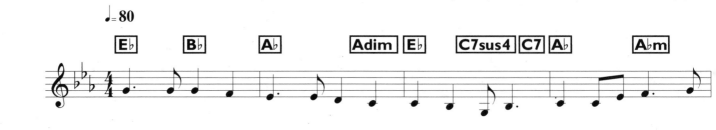

1. When you're—

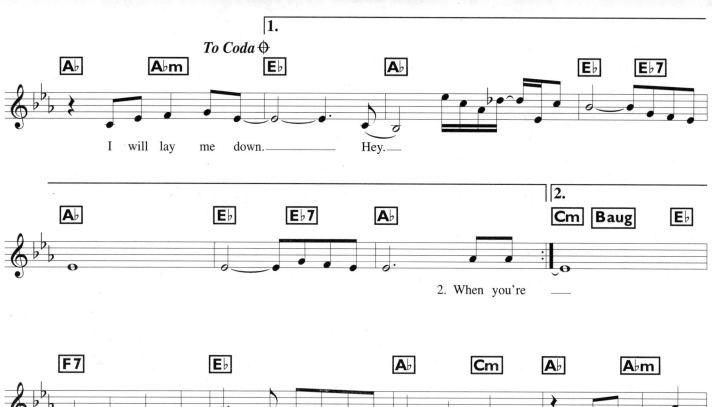

I will lay me down.____ Hey.____

2. When you're ____

F7   Eb   Ab Cm Ab Abm

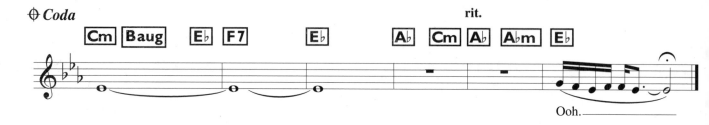

Ooh._____ Mm._____ 3. Sail on____

⊕ Coda

Cm Baug   Eb F7   Eb   Ab Cm Ab Abm Eb

rit.

Ooh._____

Verse 2:
When you're down and out, when you're on the street
When evening falls so hard, I will comfort you
I'll take your part, oh, when darkness comes
And pain is all around.

Like a bridge *etc.*

Verse 3:
Sail on silver girl, sail on by
Your time has come to shine, all your dreams are on their way
See how they shine, oh, if you need a friend
I'm sailing right behind.

Like a bridge over troubled water
I will ease your mind.

Lives of the Poets

Of the "Ode on Adversity," the hint was at first taken from "O Diva, gratum quae regis Antium;" but Gray has excelled his original by the variety of his sentiments, and by their moral application. Of this piece, at once poetical and rational, I will not by slight objections violate the dignity.

My process has now brought me to the WONDERFUL "Wonder of Wonders," the two Sister Odes, by which, though either vulgar ignorance or common sense at first universally rejected them, many have been since persuaded to think themselves delighted. I am one of those that are willing to be pleased, and therefore would gladly find the meaning of the first stanza of the "Progress of Poetry." Gray seems in his rapture to confound the images of spreading sound and running water. A "stream of music" may be allowed; but where does "music," however "smooth and strong," after having visited the "verdant vales, roll down the steep amain," so as that "rocks and nodding groves rebellow to the roar"? If this be said of music, it is nonsense; if it be said of water, it is nothing to the purpose. The second stanza, exhibiting Mars' car and Jove's eagle, is unworthy of further notice. Criticism disdains to chase a schoolboy to his common–places. To the third it may likewise be objected that it is drawn from mythology, though such as may be more easily assimilated to real life. Idalia's "velvet green" has something of cant. An epithet or metaphor drawn from Nature ennobles Art; an epithet or metaphor drawn from Art degrades Nature. Gray is too fond of words arbitrarily compounded. "Many–twinkling" was formerly censured as not analogical; we may say "many–spotted," but scarcely "many– spotting." This stanza, however, has something pleasing. Of the second ternary of stanzas, the first endeavours to tell something, and would have told it, had it not been crossed by Hyperion; the second describes well enough the universal prevalence of poetry; but I am afraid that the conclusion will not rise from the premises. The caverns of the North and the plains of Chili are not the residences of "glory and generous shame." But that poetry and virtue go always together is an opinion so pleasing that I can forgive him who resolves to think it true. The third stanza sounds big with "Delphi," and "AEgean," and "Ilissus," and "Meander," and "hallowed fountains," and "solemn sound;" but in all Gray's odes there is a kind of cumbrous splendour which we wish away. His position is at last false. In the time of Dante and Petrarch, from whom we derive our first school of poetry, Italy was overrun by "tyrant power" and "coward vice;" nor was our state much better when we first borrowed the Italian arts. Of the third ternary, the first gives a mythological birth of Shakespeare. What is said of that mighty genius is true, but it is not said happily; the real effects of this poetical power are put out of sight by the pomp of machinery. Where truth is sufficient to fill the mind, fiction is worse than useless; the counterfeit debases the genuine. His account of Milton's blindness, if we suppose it caused by study in the formation of his poem (a supposition surely allowable), is poetically true, and happily imagined. But the CAR of Dryden, with his TWO COURSERS, has nothing in it peculiar; it is a car in which any other rider may be placed.

"The Bard" appears, at the first view, to be, as Algarotti and others have remarked, an imitation of the prophecy of Nereus. Algarotti thinks it superior to its original; and, if preference depends only on the imagery and animation of the two poems, his judgment is right. There is in "The Bard" more force, more thought, and more variety. But to copy is less than to invent, and the copy has been unhappily produced at a wrong time. The fiction of Horace was to the Romans credible; but its revival disgusts us with apparent and unconquerable falsehood. INCREDULUS ODI. To select a singular event, and swell it to a giant's bulk by fabulous appendages of spectres and predictions, has little difficulty; for he that forsakes the probable may always find the marvellous. And it has little use; we are affected only as we believe; we are improved only as we find something to be imitated or declined. I do not see that "The Bard" promotes any truth, moral or political. His stanzas are too long, especially his epodes; the ode is finished before the ear has learned its measures, and consequently before it can receive pleasure from their consonance and recurrence. Of the first stanza the abrupt beginning has been celebrated; but technical beauties can give praise only to the inventor. It is in the power of any man to rush abruptly upon his subject that has read the ballad of "Johnny Armstrong,"

"Is there ever a man in all Scotland—?"

The initial resemblances or alliterations, "ruin, ruthless," "helm or hauberk," are below the grandeur of a poem that endeavours at sublimity. In the second stanza the Bard is well described, but in the third we have the puerilities of obsolete mythology. When we are told that "Cadwallo hushed the stormy main," and that "Modred made huge Plinlimmon bow his cloud–topped head," attention recoils from the repetition of a tale that, even when it was first heard, was heard with scorn. The WEAVING of the WINDING–SHEET he borrowed, as he owns, from the Northern Bards, but their texture, however, was very properly the work of female powers, as the act of spinning the thread of life in another mythology. Theft is always dangerous; Gray has made weavers of slaughtered bards by a fiction outrageous and incongruous. They are then called upon to "Weave the warp and weave the woof," perhaps with no great propriety, for it is by crossing the WOOF with the WARP that men weave the WEB or piece, and the first line was dearly bought by the admission of its wretched correspondent, "Give ample room and verge enough." He has, however, no other line as bad. The third stanza of the second ternary is commended, I think, beyond its merit. The personification is indistinct. THIRST and HUNGER are not alike, and their features, to make the imagery perfect, should have been discriminated. We are told in the same stanza how "towers are fed." But I will no longer look for particular faults; yet let it be observed that the ode might have been concluded with an action of better example, but suicide is always to be had without expense of thought.

These odes are marked by glittering accumulations of ungraceful ornaments, they strike rather than please; the images are magnified by affectation; the language is laboured into harshness. The mind of the writer seems to work with unnatural violence. "Double, double, toil and trouble." He has a kind of strutting dignity, and is tall by walking on tiptoe. His art and his struggle are too visible, and there is too little appearance of ease and nature. To say that he has no beauties would be unjust; a man like him, of great learning and great industry, could not but produce something valuable. When he pleases least, it can only be said that a good design was ill directed. His translations of Northern and Welsh poetry deserve praise; the imagery is preserved, perhaps often improved, but the language is unlike the language of other poets. In the character of his Elegy I rejoice to concur with the common reader, for by the common sense of readers uncorrupted with literary prejudices, after all the refinements of subtlety and the dogmatism of learning, must be finally decided all claim to poetical honours. The "Churchyard" abounds with images which find a mirror in every mind, and with sentiments to which every bosom returns an echo. The four stanzas, beginning "Yet even these bones," are to me original; I have never seen the notions in any other place, yet he that reads them here persuades himself that he has always felt them. Had Gray written often thus, it had been vain to blame and useless to praise him.

LYTTELTON.

George Lyttelton, the son of Sir Thomas Lyttelton, of Hagley, in Worcestershire, was born in 1709. He was educated at Eton, where he was so much distinguished that his exercises were recommended as models to his schoolfellows. From Eton he went to Christchurch, where he retained the same reputation of superiority, and displayed his abilities to the public in a poem on "Blenheim." He was a very early writer both in verse and prose. His "Progress of Love" and his "Persian Letters" were both written when he was very young, and, indeed, the character of a young man is very visible in both. The verses cant of shepherds and flocks, and crooks dressed with flowers; and the letters have something of that indistinct and headstrong ardour for liberty which a man of genius always catches when he enters the world, and always suffers to cool as he passes forward. He stayed not long in Oxford, for in 1728 he began his travels, and saw France and Italy. When he returned he obtained a seat in Parliament, and soon distinguished himself among the most eager opponents of Sir Robert Walpole, though his father, who was Commissioner of the Admiralty, always voted with the Court. For many years the name of George Lyttelton was seen in every account of every debate in the House of Commons. He opposed the standing army; he opposed the excise; he supported the motion for petitioning the king to remove Walpole. His zeal was considered by the courtiers not only as violent but as acrimonious and malignant, and when Walpole was at last hunted from his places, every effort was made by his friends, and many friends he had, to exclude Lyttelton from the secret committee.

The Prince of Wales, being (1737) driven from St. James's, kept a separate court, and opened his arms to the opponents of the Ministry. Mr. Lyttelton became his Secretary, and was supposed to have great influence in the direction of his conduct. He persuaded his master, whose business it was now to be popular, that he would advance his character by patronage. Mallet was made Under Secretary, with 200 pounds, and Thomson had a pension of 100 pounds a year. For Thomson, Lyttelton always retained his kindness, and was able at last to place him at ease. Moore courted his favour by an apologetical poem called the "Trial of Selim," for which he was paid with kind words, which, as is common, raised great hopes, that were at last disappointed.

Lyttelton now stood in the first rank of Opposition, and Pope, who was incited, it is not easy to say how, to increase the clamour against the Ministry, commended him among the other patriots. This drew upon him the reproaches of Fox, who in the House imputed to him as a crime his intimacy with a lampooner so unjust and licentious. Lyttelton supported his friend; and replied that he thought it an honour to be received into the familiarity of so great a poet. While he was thus conspicuous he married (1741) Miss Lucy Fortescue, of Devonshire, by whom he had a son, the late Lord Lyttelton, and two daughters, and with whom he appears to have lived in the highest degree of connubial felicity; but human pleasures are short; she died in childbed about five years afterwards, and he solaced his grief by writing a long poem to her memory. He did not, however, condemn himself to perpetual solitude and sorrow, for after a while he was content to seek happiness again by a second marriage with the daughter of Sir Robert Rich, but the experiment was unsuccessful. At length, after a long struggle, Walpole gave way, and honour and profit were distributed among his conquerors. Lyttelton was made (1744) one of the Lords of the Treasury, and from that time was engaged in supporting the schemes of the Ministry.

Politics did not, however, so much engage him as to withhold his thoughts from things of more importance. He had, in the pride of juvenile confidence, with the help of corrupt conversation, entertained doubts of the truth of Christianity; but he thought the time now come when it was no longer fit to doubt or believe by chance, and applied himself seriously to the great question. His studies, being honest, ended in conviction. He found that religion was true, and what he had learned he endeavoured to teach (1747) by "Observations on the Conversion of St. Paul," a treatise to which infidelity has never been able to fabricate a specious answer. This book his father had the happiness of seeing, and expressed his pleasure in a letter which deserves to be inserted:—

"I have read your religious treatise with infinite pleasure and satisfaction. The style is fine and clear, the arguments close, cogent, and irresistible. May the King of Kings, whose glorious cause you have so well defended, reward your pious labours, and grant that I may be found worthy, through the merits of Jesus Christ, to be an eye–witness of that happiness which I don't doubt he will bountifully bestow upon you. In the meantime I shall never cease glorifying God for having endowed you with such useful talents, and giving me so good a son.
        "Your affectionate father,
        "THOMAS LYTTELTON."

A few years afterwards (1751), by the death of his father, he inherited a baronet's title, with a large estate, which, though perhaps he did not augment, he was careful to adorn by a house of great elegance and expense, and by much attention to the decoration of his park. As he continued his activity in Parliament, he was gradually advancing his claim to profit and preferment; and accordingly was made in time (1754) Cofferer and Privy Councillor: this place he exchanged next year for the great office of Chancellor of the Exchequer—an office, however, that required some qualifications which he soon perceived himself to want. The year after, his curiosity led him into Wales; of which he has given an account, perhaps rather with too much affectation of delight, to Archibald Bower, a man of whom he has conceived an opinion more favourable than he seems to have deserved, and whom, having once espoused his interest and fame he was never persuaded to disown. Bower, whatever was his moral character, did not want abilities. Attacked as he was by a universal outcry, and that outcry, as it seems, the echo of truth, he kept his ground; at last, when his defences began to fail him, he sallied out upon his adversaries, and his adversaries retreated.

About this time Lyttelton published his "Dialogues of the Dead," which were very eagerly read, though the production rather, as it seems, of leisure than of study—rather effusions than compositions. The names of his persons too often enable the reader to anticipate their conversation; and when they have met, they too often part without any conclusion. He has copied Fenelon more than Fontenelle. When they were first published they were kindly commended by the "Critical Reviewers;" and poor Lyttelton, with humble gratitude, returned, in a note which I have read, acknowledgments which can never be proper, since they must be paid either for flattery or for justice.

When, in the latter part of the last reign, the inauspicious commencement of the war made the dissolution of the Ministry unavoidable, Sir George Lyttelton, losing with the rest his employment, was recompensed with a peerage; and rested from political turbulence in the House of Lords.

His last literary production was his "History of Henry the Second," elaborated by the searches and deliberations of twenty years, and published with such anxiety as only vanity can dictate. The story of this publication is remarkable. The whole work was printed twice over, a great part of it three times, and many sheets four or five times. The booksellers paid for the first impression; but the changes and repeated operations of the press were at the expense of the author, whose ambitious accuracy is known to have cost him at least a thousand pounds. He began to print in 1755. Three volumes appeared in 1764, a second edition of them in 1767, a third edition in 1768, and the conclusion in 1771.

Andrew Reid, a man not without considerable abilities and not unacquainted with letters or with life, undertook to persuade Lyttelton, as he had persuaded himself, that he was master of the secret of punctuation; and, as fear begets credulity, he was employed, I know not at what price, to point the pages of "Henry the Second." The book was at last pointed and printed, and sent into the world. Lyttelton took money for his copy, of which, when he had paid the pointer, he probably gave the rest away; for he was very liberal to the indigent. When time brought the History to a third edition, Reid was either dead or discarded; and the superintendence of typography and punctuation was committed to a man originally a comb–maker, but then known by the style of Doctor. Something uncommon was probably expected, and something uncommon was at last done; for to the Doctor's edition is appended, what the world had hardly seen before, a list of errors in nineteen pages.

But to politics and literature there must be an end. Lord Lyttelton had never the appearance of a strong or of a healthy man; he had a slender, uncompacted frame, and a meagre face; he lasted, however, sixty years, and was then seized with his last illness. Of his death a very affecting and instructive account has been given by his physician, which will spare me the task of his moral character:—

"On Sunday evening the symptoms of his lordship's disorder, which for a week past had alarmed us, put on a fatal appearance, and his lordship believed himself to be a dying man. From this time he suffered from restlessness rather than pain; though his nerves were apparently much fluttered, his mental faculties never seemed stronger, when he was thoroughly awake. His lordship's bilious and hepatic complaints seemed alone not equal to the expected mournful event; his long want of sleep, whether the consequence of the irritation in the bowels, or, which is more probable, of causes of a different kind, accounts for his loss of strength, and for his death, very sufficiently. Though his lordship wished his approaching dissolution not to be lingering, he waited for it with resignation. He said, 'It is a folly, a keeping me in misery, now to attempt to prolong life;' yet he was easily persuaded, for the satisfaction of others, to do or take anything thought proper for him. On Saturday he had been remarkably better, and we were not without some hopes of his recovery.

"On Sunday, about eleven in the forenoon, his lordship sent for me, and said he felt a great hurry, and wished to have a little conversation with me, in order to divert it. He then proceeded to open the fountain of that heart, from whence goodness had so long flowed, as from a copious spring. 'Doctor,' said he, 'you shall be my confessor: when I first set out in the world I had friends who endeavoured to shake my belief in the Christian religion. I saw difficulties which staggered me, but I kept my mind open to conviction. The evidences and doctrines of Christianity, studied with attention, made me a most firm and persuaded believer of the Christian religion. I have made it the rule of my life, and it is the ground of my future hopes. I have erred and sinned; but have repented, and never indulged any vicious habit. In politics and public life I have made public good the rule of my conduct. I never gave counsels which I did not at the time think the best. I have seen that I was sometimes in the wrong, but I did not err designedly. I have endeavoured in private life to do all the good in my power, and never for a moment could indulge malicious or unjust designs upon any person whatsoever.'

"At another time he said, 'I must leave my soul in the same state it was in before this illness; I find this a very inconvenient time for solicitude about anything.'

"On the evening, when the symptoms of death came on, he said, 'I shall die; but it will not be your fault.' When Lord and Lady Valentia came to see his lordship, he gave them his solemn benediction, and said, 'Be good, be virtuous, my lord; you must come to this.' Thus he continued giving his dying benediction to all around him. On Monday morning a lucid interval gave some small hopes, but these vanished in the evening; and he continued dying, but with very little uneasiness, till Tuesday morning, August 22, when, between seven and eight o'clock, he expired, almost without a groan."

His lordship was buried at Hagley, and the following inscription is cut on the side of his lady's monument:—

"This unadorned stone was placed here by the particular
desire and express directions of the Right Honourable
GEORGE LORD LYTTELTON,
who died August 22, 1773, aged 64."

Lord Lyttelton's Poems are the works of a man of literature and judgment, devoting part of his time to versification. They have nothing to be despised, and little to be admired. Of his "Progress of Love," it is sufficient blame to say that it is pastoral. His blank verse in "Blenheim" has neither much force nor much elegance. His little performances, whether songs or epigrams, are sometimes sprightly, and sometimes insipid. His epistolary pieces have a smooth equability, which cannot much tire, because they are short, but which seldom elevates or surprises. But from this censure ought to be excepted his "Advice to Belinda," which, though for the most part written when he was very young, contains much truth and much prudence, very elegantly and vigorously expressed, and shows a mind attentive to life, and a power of poetry which cultivation might have raised to excellence.

Printed in the United Kingdom
by Lightning Source UK Ltd.
123417UK00001B/22/A